CREATIVE ACTIVITIES
FOR
BEGINNING
MATHEMATICIANS

Written and illustrated by Sandy Baker

Good Apple

Editor: Susan Eddy

Good Apple
An Imprint of Modern Curriculum
A Division of Simon & Schuster
299 Jefferson Road, P.O. Box 480
Parsippany, NJ 07054-0480

1 2 3 4 5 6 7 8 9   MAL   01 00 99 98 97 96

DOODLE LOOPS

CONTENTS

A Word About *Math DoodleLoops*

Directions for Teachers

What Are *Math DoodleLoops*?

The activities in this book are unique learning tools that offer a stimulating way to introduce or reinforce math concepts and skills as well as language and reading comprehension. *Math DoodleLoops* integrate drawing, writing, and reading to make math concepts more relevant to children's everyday experiences. The activities are presented in three variations. Children write a math story relating to a thought-provoking illustration, illustrate a story relating to a mathematical concept, or illustrate a mathematical problem and write about it. Each *DoodleLoop* emphasizes a particular basic math skill taught at the primary level, such as counting by 5s, addition, or multiplication. For example, the concept of addition may be presented in the following three ways.

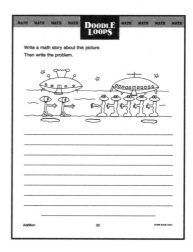

How To Use *Math DoodleLoops*

Use the corresponding *DoodleLoops* activity to introduce or reinforce a specific math skill, such as counting, addition, missing addends, or subtraction. The featured skill is noted at the bottom of each page. Introduce *Math DoodleLoops* by distributing a copy of the activity to each child. You may wish to illustrate the page on the chalkboard or on a transparency, using an overhead projector.

DOODLE LOOPS

- If the *DoodleLoops* activity presents a story that children will illustrate, you may wish to read the story to the class or have one of the children read it. Then read the directions. For example: ▶

Discuss what types of pictures children may wish to draw. You might choose to draw a picture or have one of the children create an illustration on the board or overhead transparency. Then discuss what type of math problem the story reflects. Write the correct math problem beneath the illustration. For example: ▶

- If the *DoodleLoops* activity presents a problem that children will illustrate and write about, you may wish to read the problem and the directions to the class or have one of the children do this. For example: ▶

Discuss various options for pictures that could reflect the math problem. Choose one idea to illustrate or have one of the children illustrate it on the board or transparency. Then create a group story that relates to the picture and problem. Write the story under the picture or have a child write the story. For example: ▶

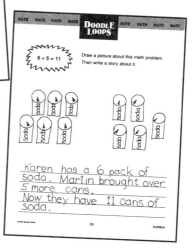

- If the *DoodleLoops* activity presents a picture that children will write about, you may wish to discuss the picture, read the directions, and ask children what math concept the picture conveys. For example: ▶

Create a group story about the picture. Write the story under the picture on the board or transparency, or ask a child to write it. Then ask children what math problem would be appropriate for the picture and story. Write the math problem at the end of the story, or ask a child to write it. For example: ▶

Be sure to promote creativity. Invite children to create clear, colorful illustrations and imaginative stories. Encourage them to take their time, to work carefully, and to come up with their own unique ideas.

Math DoodleLoops may be used to introduce a new math skill or simply to reinforce a previously introduced skill. You may wish to carefully review the directions with children each time a new concept is introduced. *Math DoodleLoops* may be used daily or when activities are pertinent to the skills you are teaching.

It is important for children to have a vehicle for sharing their *DoodleLoops* in order to reinforce their skills and ideas, to have support and feedback from their classmates, and to encourage divergent thinking. Children may share their work in a variety of ways: through group sharing, on bulletin boards, on overhead transparencies, or by inviting another class in for sharing.

Math DoodleLoops may also be used as a cooperative learning tool by inviting two or three children to work together. Children reinforce and teach each other through such an arrangement. You may wish to group children of varying levels of math proficiency or group children at the same level. Both options stimulate growth, understanding, and cooperation.

Math DoodleLoops serve as a perfect tool for portfolio assessment. They give a good indication of children's understanding of mathematical concepts, they reflect the level of children's reading comprehension, and they may also reflect children's ability to follow directions.

Family Involvement

When *DoodleLoops* are first introduced, it is helpful to write a letter to each child's family explaining their purpose. A sample letter is provided below. Encourage children to share their *DoodleLoops* with their families. The activities provide a wonderful connection between school and home, and families will enjoy sharing with their children and watching their progress over the course of the year.

Dear Family,

This year your child will be enjoying some special activities called *Math DoodleLoops*. These activities present children with a way to learn, practice, and reinforce math skills. *DoodleLoops* also serve as an excellent tool for reinforcing direction following and improving writing skills and reading comprehension.

Each *DoodleLoop* presents a math story, a math problem, or an illustration related to a mathematical situation. Children will illustrate the story and write a problem about it, illustrate the math problem and write a story about it, or write a story about the math illustration and write the corresponding math problem.

Math DoodleLoops encourage children to integrate drawing, writing, and reading to make math concepts more relevant to everyday experiences. Please take time to discuss and share these activities with your child. Thank you for your cooperation, involvement, and support.

Sincerely,

7

Directions for Parents

Math DoodleLoops offers a stimulating and exciting way to introduce or reinforce math concepts and skills. Watch your children learn to enjoy and better comprehend math concepts as they draw and write about math problems. Each *Math DoodleLoops* activity offers a challenging and unique way to learn more about specific skills, such as addition, subtraction, measurement, time telling, money values, and more!

It is important to provide some guidance as your children tackle the *DoodleLoops* activities so that each activity becomes an enriching learning experience. Your involvement and support will also make this experience more meaningful. You will be encouraging your children to integrate drawing, writing, and reading in order to help math concepts take on new clarity and meaning. Share in the fun!

It's a good idea to read the "Directions for Teachers" (see pages 4–7) before beginning *Math DoodleLoops.* You may wish to illustrate the examples on separate sheets of paper in place of the chalkboard or overhead projector used in the classroom.

Be sure your children share their work with you, other family members, or friends. Sharing helps to reinforce their ideas and gives them the opportunity for support and feedback. Encourage children to do their best work—to make clear, colorful illustrations and to write detailed, creative stories. Working slowly and carefully helps children develop a sense of pride in their finished products. Racing through the activities detracts from the learning experience. Be sure to display some examples of your child's finest work.

DOODLE LOOPS

Count and write the numbers on the lines.

Think of some things that you can count. Write about them, count them, and write your answers.

_____

_____

_____

_____

_____

Counting Skills

DOODLE LOOPS

Count the number of pennies.

Write a math story about this picture. In your story, show how you counted to find the answer. Does he buy something with the money?

_____

_____

_____

_____

DOODLE LOOPS

Fill in the numbers in order on the train. What is inside each car? Where is the train going?

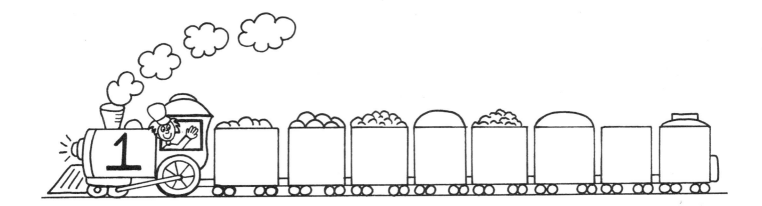

Write a math story about this picture that answers these questions.

_____

_____

_____

_____

_____

_____

_____

11   Counting Skills

DOODLE LOOPS

Fill in the numbers. How many people are in line?

What number is before 15 inside the door? What are

people waiting for?

Write a math story about the picture that
answers these questions.

_____

_____

_____

_____

DOODLE LOOPS

How many eyes does this alien creature
have altogether? Count by 2s to find out. _____

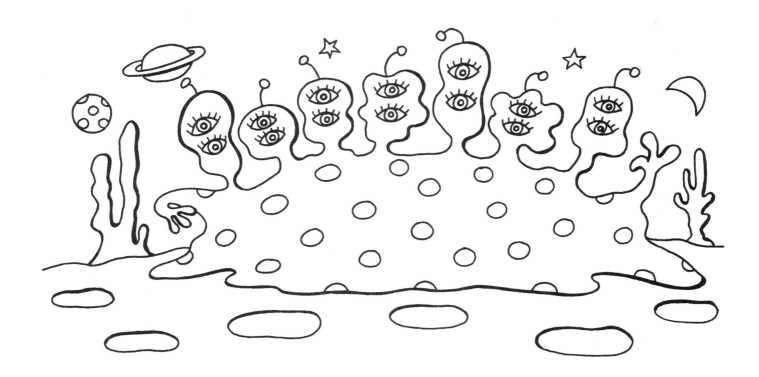

Write a math story about the picture. Show how
you counted by 2s. Tell about the alien and its
planet in your story.

_____

_____

_____

_____

_____

13   Counting by 2s

How many gifts did Barry get for his birthday? Count by 2s to find out. _____

Write a math story about this picture. Show how you counted by 2s. Tell about Barry's birthday party and what he found inside the boxes.

_____

_____

_____

_____

_____

_____

Counting by 2s   14   ©1996 Sandy Baker

DOODLE LOOPS

2 4 6 8

Draw a picture about these numbers and write a story about your picture.

_____

_____

_____

_____

DOODLE LOOPS

Count by 5s to find out how
much money Corinna has.

Write a math story about this picture. In your story,
show how you counted by 5s to find the answer.
Does she buy something with her money?

_____

_____

_____

_____

Count by 5s to find the answer.

Write a story about the picture that shows how you counted by 5s. What did they do with the finger puppets?

_____

_____

_____

_____

_____

_____

17   Counting by 5s

5   10   15   20   25

Draw a picture about these numbers and write a story about your picture.

_____

_____

_____

_____

_____

DOODLE LOOPS

Count by 10s to find out.

Write a math story about this picture. In your story,
show how you counted by 10s to find the answer.
Does Angie buy something with her money?

_____

_____

_____

_____

_____

Counting by 10s

This strange creature has 10 fingers on each hand!

How many fingers does it have altogether?

Count by 10s to find out. _____

Can you give me a hand?

Write a story about the picture. Show how you counted by 10s and tell about the creature. Where does it live?

_____

_____

_____

_____

Counting by 10s   20   ©1996 Sandy Baker

DOODLE LOOPS

10 20 30 40 50 60

Draw a picture about these numbers and write a story about your picture.

_____

_____

_____

_____

DOODLE LOOPS

Count by 3s to find out how many people Terry has in his family. Show how you found the answer and then write a story about Terry's family. _____

_____

_____

_____

_____

_____

_____

_____

MATH MATH MATH MATH

DOODLE LOOPS

3 6 9 12

Draw a picture about these numbers and write a story about your picture.

_____

_____

_____

_____

Counting by 3s

How many blocks did Matt walk to get
to the treasure? Count to find out.   _____

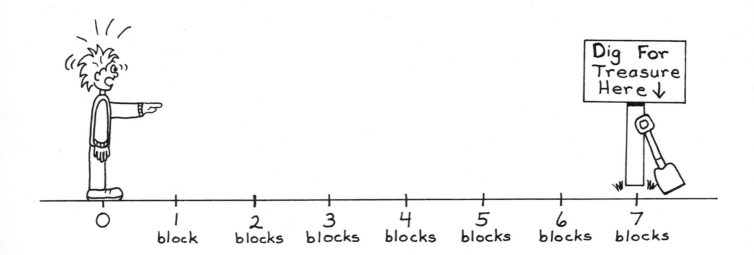

Write a story about the picture. Tell how many blocks
he walked and describe what he found.

_____

_____

_____

_____

_____

_____

DOODLE LOOPS

How many blocks did this astronaut walk
to get to the rocket? Count to find out. _____

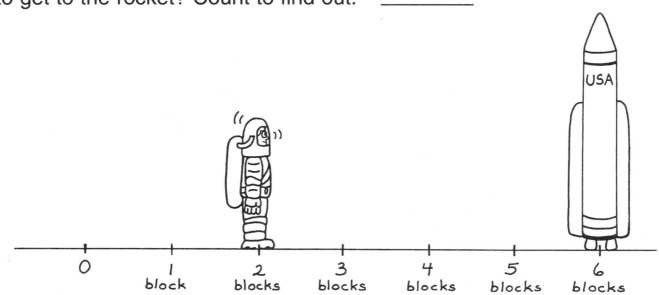

Write a story about this picture. Tell how many blocks
he walked and where he went in the rocket.

_____

_____

_____

_____

_____

_____

Lucy ate 2 whole pizzas. Her friend Fred ate 3 whole
pizzas! How many pizzas did they eat altogether?
Draw a picture about this story.

Write a math problem about your picture.

_____

DOODLE LOOPS

Jimmy stacked 9 blocks. Corky stacked 8 blocks.

How many blocks did they stack altogether?

Draw a picture about this story.

Write a math problem about your picture.

_____

27   Addition

DOODLE LOOPS

$2 + 3 = 5$

Draw a picture about this math problem.

Then write a story about it.

_____

_____

_____

_____

DOODLE LOOPS

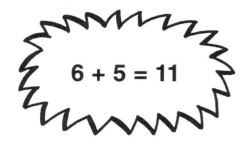

6 + 5 = 11

Draw a picture about this math problem.

Then write a story about it.

_____

_____

_____

_____

_____

DOODLE LOOPS

Draw a picture about this math problem.

Then write a story about it.

_____

_____

_____

_____

DOODLE LOOPS

Write a math story about this picture.

Then write the problem.

_____

_____

_____

_____

_____

_____

_____

DOODLE LOOPS

Write a math story about this picture.

Then write the problem.

_____

_____

_____

_____

_____

_____

_____

_____

Addition   32   ©1996 Sandy Baker

DOODLE LOOPS

Write a math story about this picture.

Then write the problem.

_____

_____

_____

_____

_____

_____

_____

Write a math story about this picture.

Then write the problem.

_____

_____

_____

_____

_____

_____

Addition   34   ©1996 Sandy Baker

DOODLE LOOPS

I would like 9 more puppies, please!

9??!

Jeremy's Pet Shop

Write a math story about this picture.

Then write the problem.

_____

_____

_____

_____

_____

_____

_____

Write a math story about this picture.

Then write the problem.

_____

_____

_____

_____

_____

_____

_____

Addition   36   ©1996 Sandy Baker

DOODLE LOOPS

I had 4 nice shirts. I got 2 dirty. How many clean
shirts did I have left? Draw a picture about this story.

Write a math problem about your picture.

_____

Subtraction

DOODLE LOOPS

Josh had 8 cookies. He ate 6 of them. How many did
he have left? Draw a picture about this story.

Write a math problem about your picture.

_____

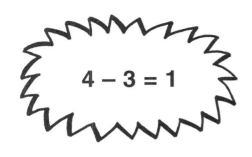

4 – 3 = 1

Draw a picture about this math problem.

Then write a story about it.

_____

_____

_____

_____

DOODLE LOOPS

3 – 3 = 0

Draw a picture about this math problem.

Then write a story about it.

_____

_____

_____

_____

DOODLE LOOPS

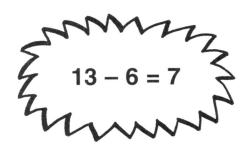

13 – 6 = 7

Draw a picture about this math problem.

Then write a story about it.

_____

_____

_____

_____

Subtraction

DOODLE LOOPS

Write a math story about this picture.

Then write the problem.

_____

_____

_____

_____

_____

_____

_____

Subtraction   42   ©1996 Sandy Baker

DOODLE LOOPS

Write a math story about this picture.

Then write the problem.

_____

_____

_____

_____

_____

_____

43

Subtraction

Write a math story about this picture.

Then write the problem.

_____

_____

_____

_____

_____

_____

Subtraction   44

DOODLE LOOPS

Write a math story about this picture.

Then write the problem.

45   Subtraction

DOODLE LOOPS

Write a math story about this picture.

Then write the problem.

DOODLE LOOPS

Write a math story about this picture.

Then write the problem.

_____

_____

_____

_____

_____

_____

_____

Subtraction

I had 3 teeth last week. Now I have 5 teeth!

How many more teeth grew in?

Draw a picture about this story.

Last Week   **This Week**

Write a math problem about your picture.

_____

DOODLE LOOPS

I ate 5 hot dogs. I was still hungry! I ate some more.

I ate 10 hot dogs altogether. How many more did

I eat? Draw a picture about this story.

Write a math problem about your picture.

_____

DOODLE LOOPS

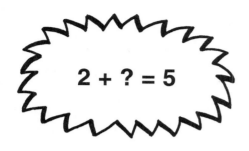

2 + ? = 5

Draw a picture about this math problem.

Then write a story about it.

_____

_____

_____

_____

_____

Missing Addends   50

DOODLE LOOPS

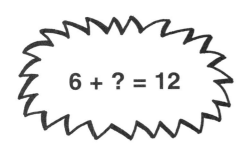

6 + ? = 12

Draw a picture about this math problem.

Then write a story about it.

_____

_____

_____

_____

_____

Write a math story about this picture.

Then write the problem.

_____

_____

_____

_____

_____

_____

Write a math story about this picture.

Then write the problem.

_____

_____

_____

_____

_____

_____

Missing Addends

DOODLE LOOPS

I had 6 teddy bears. When I got home from school,

I found only 4 teddy bears. How many were missing?

Draw a picture about this story.

Write a math problem about your picture.

_____

DOODLE LOOPS

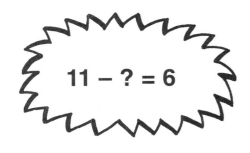

11 − ? = 6

Draw a picture about this math problem.

Then write a story about it.

_____

_____

_____

_____

_____

Write a math story about this picture.

Then write the problem.

_____

_____

_____

_____

_____

_____

_____

_____

Missing Subtrahends   56   ©1996 Sandy Baker

DOODLE LOOPS

Who took
my cookies?
I had 12 cookies!!!

Write a math story about this picture.

Then write the problem.

_____

_____

_____

_____

_____

_____

_____

Sandy Yesterday   **Sandy Today**

Write a math story about this picture.

Then write the problem.

_____

_____

_____

_____

_____

_____

_____

_____

Missing Subtrahends   58   ©1996 Sandy Baker

DOODLE LOOPS

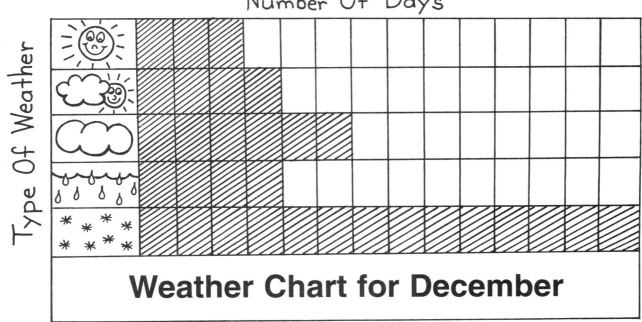

Number Of Days

Type Of Weather

Weather Chart for December

Tell as much as you can about the weather
in December.

_____

_____

_____

_____

_____

_____

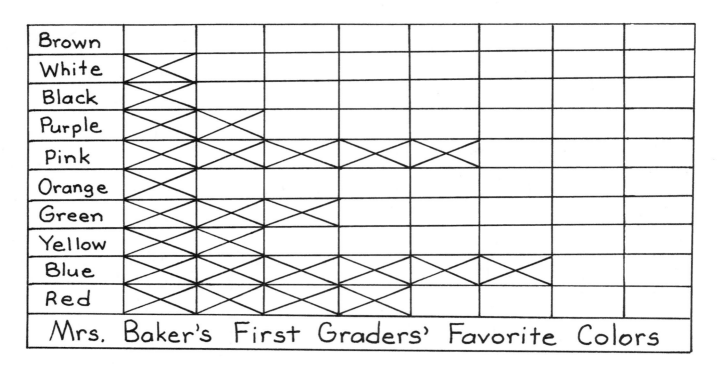

Mrs. Baker's First Graders' Favorite Colors

Tell as much as you can about these favorite colors.

_____

_____

_____

_____

_____

_____

_____

DOODLE LOOPS

On the calendar, count the days until Cookie leaves on her trip. Answer the questions below and then write a story about Cookie's trip. Tell where she goes, how she gets there, what she does, how long her trip is, and when she returns.

NOVEMBER CALENDAR						
S	M	T	W	T	F	S
				1	2	3
4	5	6	7	8	9	10
11	12	13	14	15	16	17
18	19	20	21	22	23	24
25	26	27	28	29	30	

Today is November 7th. I'm leaving for my trip on November 21st!

1. On what day of the week will she leave?_____

2. How many days until she leaves?_____

3. How many weeks until she leaves? _____

_____

_____

_____

Calendar

DOODLE LOOPS

| JULY CALENDAR |||||||
S	M	T	W	T	F	S
	1	2	③	4	5	6
7	8	9	10	11	12	13
14	15	16	17	18	19	20
21	22	23	24	25	26	27
28	29	30	31			

It's July 3rd! My birthday is in three weeks!!!

Answer the questions below and then write a story about Aggie's birthday party.

1. What is the date of Aggie's birthday? _____

2. On what day is it? _____

3. How many days until Aggie's birthday? _____

_____

_____

_____

_____

_____

DOODLE LOOPS

Use the clock to help you figure out how much time
Mark has to do his homework.

Dinner is at 6:00. How much time do I have to do my homework before we eat?

_____

Write a story about this problem. In your story, tell
how many hours Mark has to do his homework, what
he is working on, and what he's having for dinner.

_____

_____

_____

_____

Telling Time

DOODLE LOOPS

Use the clock to help you figure out how much time
Scott has to get ready for his party.

My birthday party starts at 7:00.
Now, how much time do I have
to get ready?

_____

Write a story about this problem. In your story, tell
how many hours Scott has to get ready, how he gets
ready, and what his party is like.

_____

_____

_____

_____

_____

Telling Time   64   ©1996 Sandy Baker

DOODLE LOOPS

I just put my cake in the oven. It takes 1 1/2 hours to bake. When should I take it out of the oven?

Use the clock to help you figure out when Annette should take the cake out of the oven. In your story, tell what time Annette takes the cake out of the oven and describe the cake. Why did she bake it?

_____

_____

_____

_____

_____

Telling Time

DOODLE LOOPS

Write a math story about this picture.

Then write the problem.

_____

_____

_____

_____

_____

_____

_____

Telling Time   66   ©1996 Sandy Baker

DOODLE LOOPS

I put the cookies in at 3:30.
They take 65 minutes to bake.
When should I take them out??

Write a math story about this picture.

Then write the problem.

_____

_____

_____

_____

_____

_____

Mom told me to be home in 1 hour.
I went to the park at 2:00.

Write a math story about this picture.

Then write the problem.

_____

_____

_____

_____

_____

_____

DOODLE LOOPS

Beth saved 3 dimes and 4 nickels. How much money did she save altogether? Draw a picture about this math story.

Write a math problem about your picture.

_____

DOODLE LOOPS

Len took 50¢ to the bakery. He spent 35¢ on a big
Halloween cookie. How much change did he get?
Draw a picture about this math story.

Write a math problem about your picture.

_____

DOODLE LOOPS

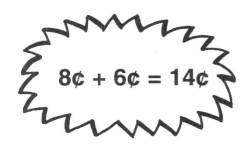

8¢ + 6¢ = 14¢

Draw a picture about this math problem.

Then write a story about it.

_____

_____

_____

_____

_____

DOODLE LOOPS

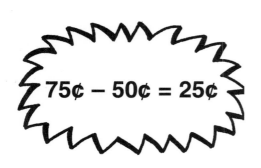

75¢ – 50¢ = 25¢

Draw a picture about this math problem.

Then write a story about it.

_____

_____

_____

_____

_____

DoodlE LOOPS

Write a math story about this picture.

Then write a problem to go with it.

_____

_____

_____

_____

_____

DOODLE LOOPS

Write a math story about this picture.

Then write a problem to go with it.

_____

_____

_____

_____

_____

Money   74

Marla built a castle that was 36" tall. Draw her castle.

Then write a story about how she built it and all of the

different ways she can measure how tall it is.

How many feet tall is it? How many yards tall is it?

_____

_____

_____

_____

_____

                                       Measurement

DOODLE LOOPS

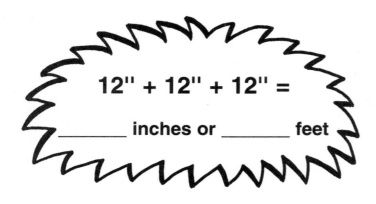

12" + 12" + 12" =

_____ inches or _____ feet

Draw a picture
about this math problem.
Then write a story about it.

_____

_____

_____

_____

_____

Measurement   76

DOODLE LOOPS

Use a tape measure to measure around your wrist,
your head, your neck, your waist, and your upper leg.
Fill in the answers.

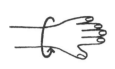 _____   _____    _____

 _____    _____

List some other things you can measure with a
tape measure. Measure them and record your
measurements.

_____ _____ _____ _____

_____ _____ _____ _____

_____ _____ _____ _____

_____ _____ _____ _____

_____ _____ _____ _____

_____ _____ _____ _____

Measurement

DOODLE LOOPS

Gail has a list of things to do today. Fill in her list and then write a story about her day.

Gail's List of Things To Do
First
Second
Third
Fourth
Fifth

Page 2
Sixth
Seventh
Eighth
Ninth
Tenth

_____

_____

_____

_____

_____

Ordinal Numbers   78   ©1996 Sandy Baker

DOODLE LOOPS

Draw a picture with a shape in it that has 3 sides and 3 angles. What is your shape called? _____

Write a story about your picture.

_____

_____

_____

_____

_____

©1996 Sandy Baker   Geometry

MATH   MATH   MATH   MATH

DOODLE LOOPS

What is this shape called?

_____

How many sides does it have? _____

How many angles does it have? _____

Turn this shape into a picture. Write about
your picture.

_____

_____

_____

_____

_____

DOODLE LOOPS

What shape do you see in this picture?

_____

How many sides does it have?

_____

How many angles does it have?

_____

Finish the picture by adding more
shapes. Write about your picture.

_____

_____

_____

_____

_____

_____

_____

                                       Geometry

Fill in the number of sides and angles under
each shape.

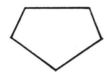      

Sides _____   Sides _____   Sides _____   Sides _____

Angles _____   Angles _____   Angles _____   Angles_____

Draw a picture using all of the shapes above. Add
details. Write a story about your shape picture.

_____

_____

_____

_____

DOODLE LOOPS

Linda and Leslie ordered one hamburger. They
wanted to split the hamburger equally. How much
did each girl have? Draw a picture about this
story and then answer the question.

_____

_____

_____

_____

       Fractions

DOODLE LOOPS

4 boys had enough money to buy one big candy bar. They each took an equal portion. How much did each boy have? Draw a picture about this story and then answer the question.

_____

_____

_____

84

DOODLE LOOPS

Can we share and
each have 1/2
of the cookies?

Cookie
Jar
(24 Cookies)

Write a math story about this picture.

Then write the problem.

_____

_____

_____

_____

_____

_____

DOODLE LOOPS

Write a story about this picture. Answer the question
below in your story. Tell what part of the pennies each
child got.

_____

_____

_____

_____

_____

_____

Fractions   86

DOODLE LOOPS

Write a story about the picture. How will the children decide how many donuts they each get? In your story, include what fraction of the total amount of donuts each child receives.

_____

_____

_____

_____

_____

　　　　　　87　　　　　　Fractions

Write a math story about this picture. Then write a
math problem.

_____

_____

_____

_____

_____

_____

Fractions and Money   88   ©1996 Sandy Baker

5 Years Old   **6 Years Old**   **7 Years Old**   **8 Years Old**

Fill in the missing numbers.

24" = _____ tens + _____ ones   44" = _____ tens + _____ ones

34" = _____ tens + _____ ones   54" = _____ tens + _____ ones

Write a story about the picture. Talk about tens, ones, inches, and feet in your story.

_____

_____

_____

_____

_____

_____

       Place Value/Measurement

Carly is sorting out her Halloween candy. She has 5 different kinds of candy, and she has 2 pieces of each kind of candy. How many pieces of candy does she have altogether? Draw a picture about this story.

Write a math problem about your picture.

_____

DOODLE LOOPS

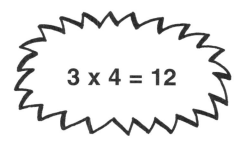

3 x 4 = 12

Draw a picture about this problem.

Then write a story about it.

_____

_____

_____

_____

_____

DOODLE LOOPS

Write a story about this picture.

Then write a problem to go with it.

_____

_____

_____

_____

_____

_____

_____

DOODLE LOOPS

Write a story about this picture.

Then write a problem to go with it.

_____

_____

_____

_____

_____

_____

Multiplication

MATH MATH MATH MATH MATH MATH MATH MATH

Stacy had 15 markers. She wanted to give an equal
number of markers to each of her 3 best friends.
How many markers did she give each friend?
Draw a picture about this story.

Write a math problem about your picture.

_____

Division   94   ©1996 Sandy Baker

DOODLE LOOPS

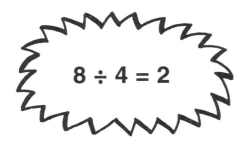

$8 \div 4 = 2$

Draw a picture about this problem and then write a story about it.

_____

_____

_____

_____

_____

DOODLE LOOPS

How many pairs of
shoes do I need?

_____

"Shoes"
Store ⟶

Write a story about this picture.

Then write a math problem to go with it.

_____

_____

_____

_____

_____

_____